SLEEP With This Book

A step by step guide to becoming a

Certified Registered Nurse Anesthetist

(CRNA)

Michael Gray, RN, BSN

Michael Gray, RN, BSN

www.sleepwiththisbook.com

SLEEP With This Book

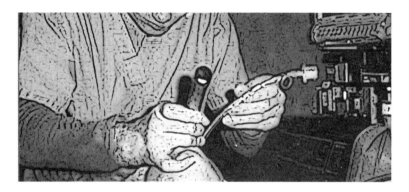

A step by step guide to becoming a

Certified Registered Nurse Anesthetist

(CRNA)

Michael Gray, RN, BSN

Copyright © 2006

Gonegray Publishing

Memphis, TN

Michael Gray, RN, BSN

Gonegray Publishing
PO Box 111196
Memphis, TN 38111-1196
www.GoneGray.com
SAN: 8 5 1 - 1 1 7 9

SLEEP WITH THIS BOOK: A STEP BY STEP GUIDE TO BECOMING A CERTIFIED REGISTERED NURSE ANESTHETIST (CRNA)

www.sleepwiththisbook.com

ISBN   0-9786270-0-8

Printed in the United States of America

Last digit is the print number: 9 8 7 6 5 4 3 2 1

Cover design by Jada Thomson (www.jadathompson.com)
Edited by Jeannette M. Meyer, Donald L. Van Pelt

Notice: This book is an instructional instrument to assist the reader in applying for an advanced role in the field of nursing. In no way should the information be used in the medical treatment of patients. Please follow all standard safety precautions. Please keep in mind that nursing is a dynamic field, therefore, information in this book is very likely to change. Reader is responsible to verify that pertinent information is current and applicable.

Special thanks to Jada, my family, friends, Christine Rimmer, Wendy Jackson, Dr. Reggie Burch, Susan Stuart, and all of the nurses and doctors who have shared their knowledge with me, especially the CVICU staff; I have been blessed with great family and friendships throughout my life, and without these, I would not be who I am today. Thank you all.

-Michael

Contents

Michael Gray, RN, BSN

Chapter One

Introduction

Chapter One
Introduction

My journey of becoming a Certified Registered Nurse Anesthetist (CRNA) started the same day that I was introduced to the idea of changing my profession to nursing. I received a telephone call from my father who said that he had met a new friend, one that was an "anesthesia nurse". This nurse traveled around the country, working for a few months in each place. This allowed him the opportunity to see the world, make great money, and have control and independence in his career path. I have always been the kind of person that enjoys helping other people. I am a compassionate person, a problem solver, intuitive, and a good teacher as well as student - all important traits for the profession of nursing. My father recognized this as he dialed my number.

Until this point in my life, I had spent six years working as a poker dealer in casinos. This job was very frustrating for me for many reasons. First, there was the ever present cloud of cigarette smoke. The environment was loud, dirty, and due to poor ergonomics, caused chronic back and neck pain. The majority of the customer base was consistently the same players, day in, day out. As a dealer, I not only watched as most of these good people ruined both their finances and health, I felt as though I contributed. This was a work environment that directly opposed my life philosophy of living healthily and happily.

I have always valued education and had been taking courses at the local community college for a few semesters with no well defined direction in mind, other than I was certain that I wanted out of the casino business. After the phone call from my father and some baseline research on the realm of nursing, I applied for the ADN program and was accepted. Two years of hard work and one NCLEX exam later, I found myself with the initials R.N. behind my name.

The goal of becoming a Certified Registered Nurse Anesthetist has stayed in my mind. I have distinct memories of almost every CRNA I have been in contact with. I once had the pleasure of having a nurse anesthetist as a patient. My experience with her was very encouraging and compelling. She stated that becoming a CRNA was one of the best decisions she had made in her life and career. During her stay, she had many visits from friends/peers that were also nurse anesthetists. There seemed to be a fellowship among this group that was unique and admirable. I have witnessed this time and again with other CRNAs I have since met, and I wanted to be able to express the same satisfaction in the choice of career paths that I have taken.

There are certain things that must be accomplished to make becoming a CRNA a reality. Some are set in stone; some are unique to each learning institution that teaches this course of study.   There are questions that each individual must answer on the road to choosing this profession.   There is also a certain acquisition of knowledge, of gaining experience, and of jumping through countless 'hoops' that must be achieved.

The following chapters will briefly describe the history and role of the certified registered nurse anesthetist.   It will describe the process of finding a school, as well as placing yourself in a position for acceptance into a program.   It will define some of the core nursing knowledge that you must possess prior to starting, as well as the hands-on experience required.

The interviewing process will also be examined, suggesting some tips and tools that will help make you successful.   Financial capability will be an important topic, since almost all programs suggest that you not work while attending this course of study.

Finally, what to expect once you are accepted and in the program will be inspected.   The didactic, or class work, that is common to most programs, will be addressed.   Also, typical clinical experiences and expectations will be described.   This will give an image of the role of SRNA (Student Registered Nurse Anesthetist) in the operating room environment, actively learning and caring for patients.

My hope in writing this book is that it finds its way into the hands of those considering nurse anesthesia as a profession.   The goal is to educate those that are already on this path, making them a more competitive candidate to the school of their choice.   It should also give an accurate enough portrayal of the challenges ahead to dissuade the faint of heart, and to motivate and solidify the ambition of those that have considered this path. Passion, enthusiasm, and hard work will pay off.

Chapter Two

Role of the CRNA

Chapter Two
Role of the CRNA

After a few years of nursing under my belt and with the completion of my BSN nearing, I felt that the time had come for me to advance my career and start researching CRNA schools. After gaining my RN licensure, I worked on an orthopedic unit for six months. I was compelled to challenge myself to acquire a wider range of skills and experience, so I worked full-time agency (per-diem and contract) in many hospitals serving the Mississippi Gulf Coast and New Orleans areas (where I am from).

I also took travel assignments as far away as Los Angeles. This allowed me exposure to a broad range of patient types, procedures, equipment, environments, documentation systems, and co-workers. With every new hospital setting, there was an increase in my ability and confidence. Among the vital tools acquired: prioritization, communication, accuracy, thoroughness, technical skills, protocol, and intuition are a few. I mention this action of changing work settings, because as a CRNA, you will likely be floated from one type of procedure to another, and possibly from one hospital to another, even in the same day.

Certified Registered Nurse Anesthetist is one of the first nursing specialty groups. According to the American Association of Nurse Anesthetists (www.aana.com),

"Over 30,000 CRNA's provide quality anesthesia care to more than 65% of all patients undergoing surgical or other medical interventions which necessitate the services of an anesthetist. In addition, CRNA's administer sole anesthesia for all types of surgical cases, from the simplest to the most complex. CRNA's are the sole anesthesia providers in two-thirds of rural hospital in the United States. CRNA's work in every setting in which anesthesia is delivered: traditional hospital surgical suites and obstetrical delivery rooms, ambulatory surgical centers and the offices of dentists, podiatrists, and plastic surgeons." *

(*Source: No Author. <u>Qualifications and Capabilities of the Certified Registered Nurse Anesthetist.</u> Retrieved and quoted from www.aana.com on April 19, 2006.)

CRNAs are included in the entire anesthesia plan. This starts preoperatively, with the physical assessment, history, and preoperative teaching. Informed consent is then obtained for anesthesia. A plan of care is devised by taking the individual patient's needs into consideration, in conjunction with those of the medical team.

Intraoperatively, the anesthetist assists in patient placement and positioning, monitors and manages changes in vital signs, administers anesthetics, and controls the patient's pain. IV's are started, central lines may be placed and invasive monitoring initiated. Thorough and accurate documentation is ongoing (this includes pre/intra/post-operatively). Also, they may administer blood products, antibiotics, intravenous fluids, and more.

Postoperatively, the CRNA is involved in the patient's recovery from anesthesia, extubation when applicable, and transfer to the post-anesthesia care unit, ICU, or wherever it is appropriate to ensure a safe recuperation.

The governmental agency that oversees accreditation for CRNA programs in the United States is The U.S. Department of Education's Council of Post Secondary Education (COPA). The Council on Accreditation of Nurse Anesthesia Educational Programs is the sole accrediting authority for CRNA programs. If you visit their website (www.ope.ed.gov/accreditation/), you can search through a current listing of all accredited schools; at the time of this writing, there are ninety-six.

The National Committee for Certifying Agencies (NCCA) sets the standards for the accreditation of certification programs (www.noca.org/ncca). The Council on Certification of Nurse Anesthetists is overseen by this authority. All graduates from nurse anesthetist programs must pass this certification prior to practicing.

Also, there is a recertification process by the AANA Council on Recertification of Nurse Anesthetists that must be maintained every two years. This ensures public safety, by verifying that there are no mental or physical problems that may hinder the provider from administering safe patient care, that the provider maintains licensure as a registered nurse, that he/she completes forty hours of continuing education (CE), and that they have been and currently are practicing anesthesia.

One illustration of the importance of the CRNA is acknowledged by worldwide organizations that are dedicated to the advancement of the Nurse Anesthetist. A few of these can be easily researched by using a web browser, or by visiting some of the sites listed in the resources chapter of this book.

One example is The International Federation of Nurse Anesthetists (www.ifna-int.org) which, according to their website, was "Founded in 1989 to advance the educational standards and practices of nurse anesthesia. Currently, there are 33 country members." This is an exciting option for those that may consider going abroad. Of course, almost all countries have their own qualifications for practice, but the interconnectivity of the field of nurse anesthesia held by this organization makes it easier to work internationally.

Some other worldwide organizations for the education and advancement of anesthetic medicine can be seen at World Federation of Societies of Anaesthesiologists (www.world-anaesthesia.org). Some of the information found at this site can be applied to working in difficult to reach environments, or ones with limited technology or available resources. Therefore, this may ultimately offer the practitioner a wider base of knowledge than they might gain from following only the traditional American education process.

As we all know, healthcare is a dynamic field. This includes changes socially, politically, and technologically. There is no guarantee that the role of Certified Registered Nurse Anesthetist is going to be steadily held in its current position of future anesthetic needs. On the contrary, the flexibility of the paradigm of nursing to adjust to the changing needs of society is one of its strongest attributes. It is very likely that the position of CRNA will be even more integral to tomorrow's anesthetic administration.

A few issues that will lead the role of the CRNA toward change are, firstly, the ever shifting code that dictates insurance coverage, specifically Medicare. The question has been presented of whether or not in the future, reimbursements will be made for more than one anesthesia provider during a case. If the answer ultimately leads to NO, does it mean that there will be more CRNA's working independently, and not under the umbrella of Anesthesiologists? Considering that it costs exponentially more to educate an Anesthesiologist than it does a CRNA, I feel that it is unlikely that the function of CRNA will be hindered.

Another issue that has arisen is the question of whether or not the role of advanced practice nurse, including certified registered nurse anesthetist, should be made mandatory to require a Doctor of Nursing Practice (DNP). The American Association of Colleges of Nursing (www.aacn.org), recommends in its *Position Statement on the Practice Doctorate in Nursing October 2004*, states:

> "The Doctor of Nursing Practice (DNP) be the degree associated with practice-focused doctoral nursing education...The practice doctorate be the graduate degree for advanced nursing practice preparation, including but not limited to the four current APN roles"

Some institutions are now considering, or are actively implementing, this change into their curriculum; changing their degree upon completion from MSN to DNP. For the SRNA student, this may ultimately mean a slightly longer curriculum than presently required.

Also, there is the role of the Anesthesia Assistant (A.A.). This is a relatively new medical profession that is currently only licensed in sixteen states (according to information obtained from www.anesthesiaassistant.com).   This number will eventually grow to compete with the CRNA for anesthesia administration. Upon the completion of this course, the graduate is granted a Masters level degree.   Admission to this program requires a Bachelor of Science, with a strong emphasis on a pre-med type curriculum. The major difference of the CRNA and Anesthesia Assistant is that the latter must administer anesthesia under the direct supervision of a qualified anesthesiologist, whereas CRNA's can act independently as providers.

I didn't mention this to shed a negative light on either certification. I believe that the field of anesthesia medicine is growing in a direction such that it will accommodate and be improved by the institution of new ideas, such as this. Some may disagree, but the economic laws of Supply and Demand and Cost/Benefit Analysis will prevail.   Both of these concepts will keep the trends in medical services heading in a positive direction, allowing the most cost effective healthcare while taking into consideration evidenced based practice and public safety.   Of course, there will be fluctuations in graphical representation of trends in these two fields, but there is a possibility that the profession of Anesthesia Assistant will increase even more the validity and usefulness of CRNA's in anesthetic care.

Chapter Three

Choosing a School

Chapter Three
Choosing a School

I am lucky to live in an area of the country that has a handful of CRNA programs within a relatively short distance from each other. Unfortunately, I felt that I might be at a disadvantage due to a less than perfect grade point average. I won't say what my undergraduate GPA is, but I will say that it is between the 3.0 and 3.5 range. I wanted to know if I would even be competitive in the pool of applicants, ensuring that I was not wasting my time by applying. I sent an e-mail to the Dean of the closest CRNA program to my home and arranged a meeting.

In this meeting, I brought a copy of my transcripts and resumé. I dressed nicely, smiled confidently, and asked her for an honest analysis of my chances. She was very optimistic and offered great suggestions, some of which I would not have thought of had I not had this meeting. Some of those things that she shared with me are mentioned in this book. She told me first and foremost that my GPA was competitive and to not be discouraged from moving forward toward my goal of becoming a CRNA.

I asked her, "If you were in my position, what would you do to give yourself the best opportunity for acceptance and success." She stated that I needed cardiovascular intensive care unit experience (CVICU). I needed experience working with vasoactive drugs and invasive hemodynamic monitoring such as PA lines. I needed to take the GRE, and to do well on it. She said that the review committee takes into consideration community service work. I should shadow a CRNA. Also, one of the major issues is that all students are strongly discouraged from working, at all. This takes a major commitment and financial planning, so prepare.

And finally, she said that if I had time, I should get the CCRN certification (see www.aacn.org). This is a certification for the professional critical care nurse that demonstrates an excellence and advanced knowledge in this field. Certain prerequisites must be met prior to obtaining this certification, such as logging 1750 hours in critical care practice within the last two years. If this interests you, there are numerous books and review courses available to help you achieve this goal.

You must have your BSN (Bachelor of Science Nursing) from an NLNAC (www.nlnac.org) or CCNE (www.aacn.nche.edu) accredited college or university. Program lengths vary, from as short as twenty-four months, to as long as thirty-six months. Thirty-one months is about the average length for most programs. This is straight through typically, with only short breaks.

The structure of the program may vary from institution to institution. Some are 'Front Loaded' with didactics, meaning that you will do most of your classroom work during the first months of the program, and the remaining time doing clinical rotations. Some mix it up with the two simultaneously, with clinicals starting shortly after the program begins. There will likely be online class work that is required, and some schools even offer web teleconferencing broadcasts of classroom time for long distance learners.

Cost of attendance varies, but ranges from around $ 27,000 for some state colleges to $ 60,000-plus for some private schools. The issue of cost will be addressed further in chapter seven. Almost every institution's tuition fees are posted on the web. Some may only post a per-hour fee. In this case, if you can download the curriculum, you should be able to get an approximation by noting the total hours accrued by completion of matriculation.

Remember to take into consideration other essential fees. Books will run you a few thousand dollars. You may be required to purchase a new computer and PDA (personal digital assistant). There may be lab and technology fees. There also may be mandatory organizational memberships to join, such as American Association of Nurse Anesthetists.

You will have to maintain your RN licensure. This is where it will be important for you to know certain things about the program's clinical affiliates. Find out where they are in relation to the school and how far they are located from where you will be living if you are accepted. Some programs may require you to drive sizable distances. This may mean that you have to maintain your RN licensure in two or three other states as well. You will also have to maintain liability insurance that will more than likely be purchased through the school.

Most schools require you to have your ACLS (Advanced Cardiac Life Support) certification, BLS (Basic Life Support), and PALS (Pediatric Advanced Life Support). These certifications will need to stay current throughout your time in the program as well. ACLS, as described briefly in chapter six, will need to be well understood. You should be able to apply them in real life, as well as in simulated cases.

You will likely need certain health records, such as a current TB skin test (PPD), tetanus, MMR, Hepatitis B series (or positive titer). You may need a current physical examination and vaccinations. Some universities offer health insurance policies to their students. This should be factored into your financial budget, since it may be mandatory to have a policy, either your own or theirs.

Each school has its own application process. You should be able to find a listing of the current accredited programs at the American Association of Nurse Anesthetist's website (www.aana.com). I suggest that you compare schools. That way you can determine which ones best fit your unique situation. For instance, some require certain prerequisites, such as organic/biochemistry, physics, and/or biostatistics. Some may offer these courses as co-requisites. So, if you already have some of these courses, it may lighten your load a bit. Also, by knowing this information it may be possible to take one or two of the classes, even prior to getting into the program. Why would you do this, you may ask? Well, if you feel that you may be borderline competitive (due to a suboptimal GPA for instance), taking a graduate level course, especially at the institution where you are applying, will give the perception that you are serious about this course of study, as well as capable of doing well at this level didactically.

The lowest acceptable GPA for an applicant to any school that I researched was 2.75, with a 3.0 average of the last 60 hours. Some also take a compilation of the fundamental science courses (Chemistry, Microbiology, Statistics, etc.) and compare this average with the overall GPA. Depending on the size of the class to be admitted and the applicant pool (which varies each application cycle), you may need a much higher GPA to be competitive. That is one reason why I suggest researching each individual program, and if possible, corresponding with the head of the program to get a feel of where you need to be academically.

Some schools mandate taking the GRE or Graduate Record Examination (see Education Testing Service (ETS) at www.ets.org/gre). Some may simply recommend that you take it, and some do not require it at all. Also, a handful of schools may require you to take the MAT or Millers Analogies Test (see www.milleranalogies.com). In either case, purchase a workbook, along with computerized testing software (usually accompanying the book), and practice prior to taking the test.

All schools have individual parameters that they would like the applicant to achieve or surpass. The GRE has three sections. First, there is an analytical writing section with a possibility scoring of 0-6 pts, which according to ETS, "looks for critical thinking and analytical writing skills, not grammar and mechanics." This section is scored in half point increments. Then there is the verbal section with a score of 200-800, and a quantitative section with a score of 200-800. For example, Samford University at the time of this writing states that they require minimum acceptable scores of 450 verbal, 520 quantitative, and 4 for analytical writing.

Along with submitting official transcripts from all academic institutions that you have ever attended, you will also need to write an application essay. There may be certain parameters that vary from institution to institution. For instance, one may state that it must be one and only one page, where another may want it (around) three pages. The length restriction is going to determine what you can write about.

What is it that they are looking for? Can you speak and write using the English language professionally and expertly? Are you thorough and accurate, meaning, are there no grammatical errors? Proofread it and have others proofread it also. Do yourself and them a favor; don't submit a poorly written paper with errors.

Use nursing terminology, such as: improved outcomes, patient advocacy, promotion of health and wellness, etc. Write about why you want to be a CRNA. Why will you make a good CRNA? What experiences have you had with CRNAs? Why did you choose THIS particular school that you are applying to? What have you done to place yourself in a position for success in relation to this goal? They want to know who you are and why you should be chosen. How will you be an attribute to the profession of nurse anesthetist?

Now, try putting that all into one to three pages. You will have to cut and paste, amend, and then make your paper even more concise. Have someone in the medical field read it and mark it up with a red pen. Revise it again. Red pen it again. Do that about ten times until you have your masterpiece. Then submit it to the school, hold your breath, and cross your fingers; praying that you didn't forget to 'dot an I or cross a T' (which you can't forget to do using a word processor anyway). Oh, that reminds me, use a common font like Times New Roman or Arial. Print it on high quality paper, preferably the same paper on which you will print your resumé. A lot of colleges now have online application processes that will alleviate this need.

As just stated, you will also need a well-designed professional/academic resumé. This document should not be taken lightly. Research what an excellent resume looks like. Most word processor programs, such as Microsoft Word, have templates to assist you in creating a decent looking resumé. But, do you want what you submit to be a decent, generic looking document? Or, do you want the quality of your work to resemble the meticulous attention that you are going to apply to all of your work once you get into the program? Don't be lazy. The help is out there. Take the extra time and produce an excellent product.

You will need {professional} references. Some institutions have downloadable forms that you may (or in some instances, must) use for your references. One example of a reference form from the University of Tennessee Memphis CRNA program asks the reference to address: "Intellectual ability, competence in nursing, leadership, creativity/innovation, cooperativeness, dependability, motivation, self-discipline, initiative, integrity, analytical skills, oral skills, and written skills."

The letters must come from professional sources. The Dean of your undergraduate degree is usually a good reference. Therefore, if you are still acquiring your BSN, make sure that this person knows who you are. This way, when you ask him or her for a reference, he or she will know you personally and will not be giving reference to just your transcripts.

You will also very likely want to get a reference from the nurse manager in the Intensive Care Unit where you have acquired your requisite experience. Do you know of any Certified Registered Nurse Anesthetist's that would be willing to give you a good reference? Try to get your references from MSN or better sources. Do you personally know any Anesthesiologists or Surgeons that would make a good source for reference?

Remember, usually these letters of recommendation are sent directly to the Office of Admissions, sealed. You may not even know what is said in some cases. So choose your references carefully, always asking for an honest and fair assessment of your ability to function in the role of advanced nursing practice.

Your experience and professional relationships will be inherently represented by the quality of your references. Make sure that you nurture these relationships, that you have acquired the type of experience that will put you on the path to success, and for heavens sake, don't burn any bridges!

Chapter Four

Required Experience

Chapter Four
Required Experience

The prerequisite experience for all CRNA schools is that you must have a minimum of one year's experience in an acute care nursing setting. In essence this amounts to at least one year in a critical intensive care unit (ICU), but it is ultimately determined by each individual program. Does emergency room experience, peri-operative or post-anesthesia experience count towards this requirement? Sometimes. But most programs will tell you, "No, Nope, Sorry." On one rare occasion, I have heard of someone with a few years of pediatric ICU experience, along with less than one year of adult ICU experience being admitted to a program, but this was an exception that I am only mentioning so someone doesn't write me an e-mail, saying, "But, But, But..." You need the experience. There is a reason for it being a prerequisite.

The day after the meeting (which I mentioned earlier) with the Dean of the CRNA program, asking what steps I needed to take to get in, I set up a meeting with the Nurse Manager of the CVICU (cardiovascular intensive care unit). Two weeks later, after giving notice where I was working, I started my orientation process with a preceptor in CV. She was a nurse that had been working CVICU for about three years. Guess why? She was going to CRNA School. On top of that, she was already an Advanced

Registered Nurse Practitioner. Are we going in the right direction? For me, this was just one more affirmation.

The Nurse Manager told me that she has sent around fifteen people from her unit to CRNA school. I was apprehensive at first to tell her that I had aspirations of CRNA school, fearing that it may have negative connotations because of the employee turnover. She stated, to the contrary, that CRNA applicants are very valuable employees. They are highly motivated, focused, and dependable. They are there to learn. They are dedicated to their goals and direction, knowing that the experience of the environment is a motivating factor for going in to work each day. They are usually good mentors and preceptors (as exhibited by my own). And, she knows that they will be there for at least a year and a half or two, while waiting to get into the program. All of this makes us great prospects for employment.

What if you can't get into a CVICU? Maybe there are no positions open. If this is the case, be tenacious; follow up at a later date. Maybe there is none in the area where you live; then look for a high acuity Med-Surg ICU or Neuro ICU, preferably at a level-one trauma center if there is one in your area.

Why is CVICU preferable, you may ask? This answer is easily answered by first addressing another topic: Shadowing. If you want to get the most advantageous experience shadowing a CRNA, then I suggest that you follow one that is doing a cardiac case, such as a Coronary Artery Bypass Graft (CABG) or a valve replacement (AVR, MVR). Often times, Anesthesiologists do these, and if this is the case, try to shadow one as well. The experience will likely expose you to the pre-op assessment and pt-education, patient placement intraoperatively, intubation, induction of anesthesia, IV placement, arterial line, intra-jugular central line, pulmonary artery (PA) Swan-Ganz catheter, cardiopulmonary bypass (CPB) by the perfusionist, hemodynamic monitoring and management, and maybe TEE (trans-esophageal echocardiogram). This is not a comprehensive list, but gives the picture.

As an SRNA, you will be doing these cases. As an anesthetist, the pharmacological tools you use to manage emergencies (hyper/hypotension, arrhythmias, pulmonary challenges), in most cases, are frequently the same ones that are used in these cases. The exposure to the physiology, pathophysiology, and management of these cases are invaluable to witness as an SRNA candidate. You may also be fortunate enough to witness a CRNA precepting an SRNA in the operating room environment, where you can observe the interaction.

What I did was this: I set up a meeting with the director of peri-operative services at the facility where I worked. I introduced myself, and explained to her my professional goals. I asked her if it would be possible to shadow intraoperatively. She agreed. What we decided on was every Monday (on my own time), from 7-3, I was placed with an RN circulator. I chose the types of cases that I wanted to see, and once in the OR, was able to float over to the Anesthetist or Anesthesiologist. Some times they were teaching a student, but all were receptive to my observing and learning.

What I learned was invaluable. It increased my confidence in knowing that this was definitely something that I could do, and that I wanted to do. It showed me that the statement, "Nurses eat their young", does not apply here. I once heard in nursing, "Learn a skill. Do a Skill. Teach a Skill." This is what I have observed; the experienced practitioner believed in the transfer of knowledge and educating those that wanted to learn. I am not sure if this is out of duty, or love of the job, but the latter seems to be what I observed and feel takes place. I spent twelve days, or three months of Mondays, shadowing in the OR. This was the most encouraging and rewarding experience, deepening my passion towards this life choice I am making.

My goal for shadowing intraoperatively was multi faceted. First, I wanted to make sure that this career direction was the one that I really wanted to take. Secondly, I wanted to acquire a baseline knowledge by observing from the sidelines, asking questions when they arose (which was often), and soaking in the experience like a sponge to water. Thirdly, I knew that if I could put in hours intraoperatively, it would allow me to hopefully network with those that might be willing to give me an important reference into the program. And last, but not least, I felt that this would be one more thing that helped me stand out from the other applicants.

In CVICU, the CABG patient, AVRs, MVRs, and other critical heart procedures come directly from the operating room table to their room in the ICU. They remain intubated and placed on the ventilator. They usually have chest tubes that are connected to suction, and closely monitored for output. Their PA Swan-Ganz is connected to the SVO2 monitor and zero'd (ensuring accurate calibration). The Arterial lines and CVP (central venous pressure) lines are zero'd as well. Some may have an IABP (intra-aortic balloon pump) requiring monitoring. I will not go over what the normal values of these monitoring tools are, but this is something that you will need to eventually know.

Sometimes these patients come up with continuous vasoactive drips, titrated to control blood pressure, contractility, and/or heart rate. There may be a continuous insulin infusion running, requiring frequent blood glucose monitoring. Blood products such as PRBC's (packed red blood cells), FFP (fresh frozen plasma), and platelets may be hanging or ordered to be infused. Colloids such as Albumisol may be needed for intravascular volume expansion.

You will also get to watch the progression of ventilator weaning. Optimally, these patients go from CMV to CPAP (varying degrees of ventilation), to extubation in a few hours, and then are up to a chair shortly thereafter. This in itself is an amazing thing to witness after viewing a few of these cases intraoperatively. Often times, co-morbidities such as COPD (chronic obstructive pulmonary disease) prevent patients from being extubated this quickly. Some may be placed on Propofol (Diprovan) or Lorazepam (Ativan) drips for sedation.

Stat serum labs will be sent to the laboratory. Urine output will be monitored. Lung sounds, heart sounds, pulses, dressings, temperature, ABG's, and on and on. Sounds complicated? Impossible? Well it is not. You will not be alone either, as a CVICU nurse, or as a CRNA. But, you may be in charge and responsible for making the majority of the decisions for the care and management of this patient. As a CRNA, some cases may have this much and more going on at the same time, so the idea is for you to get familiar and comfortable with all of these things prior to walking in to the OR for the first time and not having to learn all of this then.

What type of drugs should you be familiar with and why? Some of the most commonly used drugs are:

- Dobutamine
- Dopamine
- Atropine
- Epinephrine
- Norepinephrine (Levophed)
- Nitroprusside (Nipride)

- Nitroglycerine (Nitro)
- Phenylephrine (Neosynephrine)
- Milrinone (Primacor)
- Cardizem
- Amiodorone

I did not define these drugs for you. I did this intentionally. There is no way that I can print the Nurses Drug Reference or PDR for each of the drugs. Also, there may be certain facility specific parameters for some of these drugs that you need to be familiar with, such as maximum dosage. You should be familiar with the following for each:

- Classification
- Indications for use
- Mechanism of action
- Pharmacokinetics
- Contraindications
- Adverse reactions and side effects
- Interactions
- Route and Dosage
- Assessment/Frequency of monitoring

It is necessary to be familiar with some key terms involved in cardiovascular dynamics. Next, I have listed terms that you must be familiar with. Space has been left on the side for you to get your medical dictionary out, or do some research online, and define these for yourself. You have gotten this far in the book, which shows that you are motivated. It is important for you to learn these, and if I give you short definitions, this may prevent you from doing further research into these concepts. One great thing about the internet is hypertext links (the underlined word on a webpage that links you to another webpage of that particular subject). My hope is that you will go to a web browser, search a specific term, and will be led on a journey that will increase your knowledge of things that I do not have listed here, as well as see the correlation between some of these dynamics. Bookmark your favorite websites, making a list of important resource sites that you have come across. Also, write in this book. Take a pen and make notes. Mark it up, draw arrows, write definitions, cross out things that you don't think work for you and circle things that do.

- Stroke Volume
- Systemic Vascular Resistance
- Vasoconstriction
- Vasodilatation
- Contractility
- Preload
- Afterload
- Inotropic
- Chronotropic
- Dromotropic
- Agonist
- Antagonist
- Ace-inhibitor
- Calcium Channel blocker
- Beta blocker
- Starling's Law of the Heart
- Adrenergic
- Cholinergic
- Nicotinic

- Muscarinic
- Catecholamines
- Normal value ranges for CVP, PA, MAP, ICP, CPP, SVO2, CI, CO, formulas to calculate, and why these values would be increased or decreased.

You need to be able to recognize electrocardiogram rhythms (EKG/ECG). One of my favorite websites is www.ecglibrary.com, which gives descriptions of what and why a normal rhythm is a normal rhythm, and the rationale for specific rhythm abnormalities. It may not be necessary for you to be able to read 12-lead EKGs, but if you have this skill, you will be ahead of the curve.

At **www.sleepwiththisbook.com**, there is a set of index cards available with broad definitions of most of the previously stated dynamics, formulas, and drugs. I suggest you come up with a system for learning these concepts, for even if you do not continue on the road of becoming an anesthetist, they will make you a more informed nursing professional.

Some programs have available online a listing of the required books needed throughout the program. Some schools, such as Arkansas State University, require you to read Basics of Anesthesia, by Robert Stoelting and Ronald Miller (which I suggest you do before going on your interview). While browsing the internet one day, I ran across a web log by someone saying that it was a bad idea to purchase any books and to start reading before you actually get accepted. Well, needless to say, I EMPHATICALLY DISAGREE! What kind of thinking is that? By beginning your initiation to Anesthesia terminology and concepts, you give yourself an opportunity for establishing baseline knowledge to start the program with. This will also make your shadowing experience(s) more valuable.

Let me just shoot off some terminology that you may have never heard before: MAC (minimum alveolar concentration), Pbr (partial pressure of the brain), Pa (arterial blood partial pressure), ED (effective dose), PA (alveolar partial pressure), Isoflurane, Desflurane, Sevoflurane, Agent specific vaporizers, LMA (laryngeal mask airway), PS-1 thru 6 (physical status classification of the American Society of Anesthesiologists), and malignant hyperthermia. Do you need to know what these things are prior to starting the program? Probably not. If you do, will you be at an advantage (in comparison to where you would have been personally had you not initiated yourself to this field)? YES.

As an anesthetist, you will need to have a nursing library, expanding the one that you have likely already acquired throughout nursing school. But guess what? These books are expensive. Some, very expensive. There is a way to get around this though, at least until you are required to buy specific editions of books by specific authors, as will be the case when you start your first semester.

For now though, go online to Amazon (www.amazon.com), a1books.com, cheaptextbooks.com, overstock.com, or any other online source that you are familiar with that offers discounted and used books (sometimes Ebay has some as well). Search for past editions and used books. It doesn't matter if they are highlighted, dog-eared, or coffee stained. I spent about $120 and purchased 10 books. An average of twelve dollars for one-hundred dollar books is a great deal, and a great investment in your future.

In the resource section at the end of this book is a listing of titles that I have personally purchased, as well as others that you may find valuable for your own library. When deciding what books to purchase, I looked for books that either sounded familiar from lists that I researched from anesthetist programs, that sounded good and were super inexpensive, or in areas where I thought I might be lacking knowledge. The choice, as in everything else is yours.

Chapter Five

Community Service

Chapter Five
Community Service

I am assuming that most reading this book have heard of the Golden Rule: "Treat others as you would have them treat you." Whether or not you follow this simple moral precept is a pretty significant indicator on how you treat other people. This is exhibited in your communication and interactions with others, as well as represented in your patient care within the medical setting. How many times have you thought to yourself as a practitioner, "If this was my family member, how would I want them treated?" (If you have never asked yourself this question, maybe it is time to start.)

As a CRNA, you will be doing pre-operative teaching, including educating and answering questions about risks from anesthetics. Clients will TRUST you with their lives, and as a CRNA, you have the ability to be the most important patient advocate of the intraoperative team. If you work in an environment in cooperation with Anesthesiologists, others will depend on your integrity and trustworthiness; the type of person that you are. Experiences outside of nursing, doing good for goodness' sake, will show in your actions inside of nursing.

The next question I pose is this, if you were already a CRNA, as well as part of a selection committee for future CRNAs, what type of person would you prefer to admit into your program? If you had to choose between a student with a 3.90 GPA and no extracurricular activities and a student with a 3.55 GPA that also has proven by his community activities and promotion of health to be a very well rounded person of high moral and ethical standards, who would you likely decide on?

How you did over all in your scholastic career thus far is a pretty good indicator on how you will do in the future and if you will be able to handle the advanced course load of CRNA School, true. But there are factors that may have affected your GPA that are taken into consideration. You may have had acute health problems or relational difficulties that affected your performance. So, there really might not be too large of an intellectual difference between the 3.90 and the 3.55 student. On the other hand, the things you DO are very definable and significant indicators of the kind of person that you are. If you have never done any volunteer or community service, then you have never done it. It is as simple as that. And if you have, then you will stand out in a crowd of similarly dressed individuals, with similar GPAs, and similar stories to tell, but with no community service to mention. Make yourself a more valuable member of society and you will also make yourself more valuable as a professional nurse.

Have you ever heard the phrase, "When the student is ready, the teacher will appear"? It is similar with the 'Giving of Self'. I remember the day that I was ready to take the step from knowing about the dynamic of volunteering, to actually becoming someone who does community service on my own volition. I picked up a small local paper and immediately found an ad looking for Hospice volunteers. Actually, I didn't look for it, it found me.

I will briefly discuss some ideas on volunteering in your community. What you find will be equivalent to what you are ready for. It is not necessary for it to be related to the realm of nursing, though, improving patient outcomes and promotion of health are optimal directions to go in my opinion, since this is your specialty.

As a nurse, one of the most rewarding aspects of the job is therapeutic communication. We have the ability to educate patients and families. Through assessment of needs, communication styles, and forms of teaching, we can have a strong influence on a patient's state of health, both mentally and physically. Unfortunately, sometimes the duties of nursing, such as charting and medication administration, prevent us from accomplishing the active listening and individualized care that we would like to perform.

I am a volunteer for Hospice, which is a community service that provides end of life and palliative care for the terminal patient and their families. Not all hospices are exactly the same, but most offer nursing services, aids for ADL (Activities of Daily

Living) assistance, case management, spiritual support, volunteers, and other services.

As a volunteer for Hospice, I am able to focus one on one with the client and family. I am temporarily unburdened by nursing duties, allowing me time to focus on therapeutic communication. Sometimes it is as simple a task as caregiver relief for someone caring for a terminal relative that makes all the difference in the world. Other times, the patient may just be lonely, or want to talk to try to find closure. In this case, you actively listen. You may be able to facilitate reconciliation between family members that have lost contact. Not to sound ambiguous, but this dynamic is complex and simple at the same time, both challenging and rewarding. The premise is this though...You are unselfishly giving your time and energy to those in need.

What else can you do along these lines? If you are ambitious enough you can start from scratch by planning your own community service project. Using the nursing process (Assessment, Diagnosis, Planning, Implementation, and Evaluation), you can formulate a plan. An example of this would be as follows:

Assessment: Listen to the community. What is needed? Ask questions.

Diagnosis: What is the best project? Is it valuable to the community? How will you recruit help? Fundraising? Are there liability issues to contend with?

Planning: Organization. Data collection. Leadership. Define time, dates, transportation, and responsibilities.

Implementation: Training of others involved. Assignment of individual expectations and goals to be achieved. Get started!

Evaluation: Were the goals met? Could it have been done more effectively/efficiently? What were the major difficulties? What were the major rewards for all involved?

This plan can be used for all aspects of community improvement. Some ideas might be:

- Help initiate a local blood drive
- Influence the political process to make changes in healthcare policy
- Improving conditions of community parks
- Become a facilitator to increase volunteerism from other members of the community
- Stage a fundraising campaign for a specific need
- Assist with charity auctions
- Organize a clothing donation drive for the homeless
- Organize a food drive for the local food bank
- Become a camp nurse for special needs children
- Sit with patients in nursing homes and Alzheimer's units

- Habitat for Humanity (www.habitat.org)

- Red Cross (www.redcross.org)

- United Way (www.unitedway.org)

- Good Will (www.goodwill.org)

- Salvation Army (www.salvationarmyusa.org)

- Mentor nursing students

- Big Brother/Big Sisters (www.bbbsa.org)

- Go to a web browser and search Community Service Ideas

- Volunteermatch.org

No matter what type of community service endeavors you choose, you cannot lose. Usually there will be no one grading your performance, just an immediate sense of achievement within yourself, knowing that you did a good job. You may even receive gratitude from those benefiting, but this is neither a necessity, nor should it be the motivation for your actions. Are you ready? Then take the first step (if you haven't already) and get moving...I'll see you there.

Chapter Six

Interviewing

Chapter Six
Interviewing

Here are some of the types of questions you may have right now: What should I expect on the interview? How should I dress? How should I present myself? What questions might be asked of me? What type of questions should I ask?

The number one advice I can give is this: Be prepared! How do you do this? Well, for starters, doing research, searching the web, and asking questions. Following the ideas in this book might be considered another. If you put yourself in a position for success, you are more likely to succeed. A simple philosophy, but one overlooked by many. You put yourself in a position for success by preparing, then acting efficiently and effectively towards a certain goal.

Think about the concept of reverse engineering: If you were a professional anesthetist or anesthesiologist, what type of person would you want to have working as your peer? Would you want this person to be a confident, competent, dependable, and flexible person? Would you want this to be a professional person of high integrity, with high self-standards, as well as being intellectually and emotionally capable to handle the challenges of this field? Of course you would, so...be that person!

When you consider the job of the interviewing committee, they are probably the most important link to your entrance into the program. Yes, letters of recommendation are important. Yes, GPA is a good indicator to academic prowess. Yes, the type and length of your experience is highly important. The entrance essay? How much can you say in one to three pages that is going to turn the table in your favor? All of these things that are reviewed during the application process will be reflected by your performance at the interview.

Do your homework. Keep a journal. Conduct your own interviews with CRNAs and SRNAs that you come in contact with. Make notes of what you have learned about the institution that you are interviewing at. Who are the main members of the faculty? Who is the Dean? What is the name of the Director of Admissions? If you know this information, it may come in helpful when you are sitting across a desk with some individuals that may effect the direction of the rest of your life. Just a thought.

How long has the anesthesia program been in place? What are the average class sizes? What facilities does this program use for clinical sites and how far are they from where you will be living if accepted into the program? Knowing the answer to these types of questions will allow you to make better use of your time during the interview, focusing on questions related to more important things that will give them a better idea of who you are as a person.

Now for the obvious: Before the day arises, go to the location where the interview will be and familiarize yourself with parking, traffic, directions, etc. Be on time. No, be early. Eat a light, highly nutritious breakfast and make sure that you get plenty of rest the night before. Turn off your cell phone and pagers!

I remember once as a child asking my mother how much water it took to water a plant; how did you know when it was enough? She said, "If you were a plant, how much water would you want? Then give yourself even a little more." As far as what you need to wear to the interview, ask yourself how much you need to dress up to look professional? Then do that, and a little more. You will be judged by your appearance. Look your best.

What will the interview consist of? All institutions are different. The interview may take place with two, three, or more interviewers simultaneously. These may be members of the faculty, admissions, or even senior students of the program that you are applying for. The interviews may also be done with certain faculty members individually.

There are things that interviews for most institutions have in common and we will focus on these similarities. They want to know about your experience. They want to know if you are intellectually capable to handle the course load. They want to see that you can communicate effectively, being able to articulate responses to difficult questions, using critical thinking. They need to know that you are an ethical person. They also want to know that you can afford to go to the program without having excessive financial commitments; most will strongly encourage you not to work at an outside job at all.

Some general questions that may be asked might sound like this:

- Tell me about yourself, describe yourself? (Do NOT be cocky!)
- What do you consider your greatest strengths?
- What are your weaknesses?
- Describe a time that you had to react quickly to a situation?
- What ways in your nursing career have you exhibited leadership?
- Why did you determine this career choice?
- What is the most mentally demanding thing you have done?
- What have you done in the ways of community service or volunteerism?
- Tell me about a situation in a code that you feel could have been done better and why?
- Tell me about your ICU experience and how you feel it has prepared you for this program?

Some nursing questions may sound like:

- Describe methods to decrease ICP (intracranial pressure)

- A patient that was in 2nd degree heart block is now in 3rd degree block, with a rate of 30 beats per minute and cyanotic. What are you going to do next? (Make sure you know ACLS protocols!)

- What experiences have you had with CRNAs in your career?

- What are some of the signs of Nipride toxicity?

- What would some reasons be for a patient to have hyperkalemia?

- What signs and symptoms would a patient with cardiac tamponade exhibit?

- What area some of the signs and symptoms of thyroid storm (thyrotoxicosis)?

- What are some risks for renal dysfunction?

- What are some leading factors for cardiac dysrhythmias?

Use professional language (do not use slang). Be concise, but don't be vague. Be honest in your answers. Another suggestion is to write these questions (and ones of your own) on index cards with your answers on the back and review them. Ask your significant other, friend, or peers to practice interviewing you. Perfect practice makes perfect.

There are really two interviews taking place. They are interviewing you, and you are interviewing them. They are assessing the latter by the types of questions that you ask. This lets them know that you have researched the subjects important to you, are able to ask intelligent questions, not intimidated, and it gives them a little more information on how your mind works.

Take notes (you can ask their permission if you would like). You can bet that they are taking notes. It will show that you are attentive and organized, but remember that you don't want to look like you are standoffish, have OCD, or are unable to make solid eye contact. Practice taking notes while maintaining eye contact. PDA's (personal digital assistants) are commonly used, especially in the medical field. It is likely that you may be required to use one in the program. You might even be asked if you use it in your role already as an RN. Have a drug reference program on your PDA and be familiar with it if you already aren't.

Write down a list of these questions prior to interviewing. Ask others that have interviewed, are currently SRNAs, or are CRNAs already, what would be good questions to ask. Ask open-ended questions that are not too complex. Don't disrupt their response after they begin to respond. Avoid easy no brainier questions that you should already know the answers to.

Some examples of questions you might ask are:

- Does this facility have a Human Patient Simulator? Adult and pediatric? (see www.meti.com)

- How do I compare with the other candidates interviewed?

- Is there anything else that you need from me to have a complete picture of my qualifications?

If you are a person prone to performance anxiety, I strongly suggest that you become familiar with visualization techniques. This is a great stress reduction and performance enhancing tool. The simple premise is that you imagine yourself in the interview, sitting at the desk across from a review committee, calmly, confidently answering questions. You should set aside specific time to practice this over and over, preferably in a quiet environment.

Go over the entire morning in your head. Close your eyes. Imagine yourself getting dressed for the day. You leave your home early so that you will have time to spare; you are not rushed. You arrive; introducing yourself to those that are expecting you. You are calm and confident, with an assuring smile. You have a healthy posture, maintaining solid eye contact with your interviewers and peers. Since you have prepared yourself for some expected question types, most of your answers are well organized, thorough, and intelligent.

Some questions asked are unexpected, difficult to answer; but you do not allow yourself to get stressed. You simply consider the questions, recalling your experience and knowledge, and give the best answer you can. You do well. You ask good questions. You feel that you have been received in a positive manner and leave feeling confident and pleased with your performance.

It is not uncommon to have to apply more than once to an institution. Acceptance into these programs is very competitive. Sometimes, especially if you have a less than outstanding undergraduate GPA, you may have to display a bit of tenacity, showing that you REALLY, REALLY want to do this. So, if after all is said and done, and you are not accepted your first time, do not give up.

Use this as a learning experience, making notations in your journal about things you will do better next time, things you feel that were important, and note any feedback that the interviewing committee might have given you. Do not take 'no' as an answer. Apply to numerous schools. Put yourself in a position for success and improve your value as a candidate for next time.

Michael Gray, RN, BSN

Chapter Seven

Paying for School

Chapter Seven
Paying for School

I asked one SRNA that I spoke with what types of questions were asked in her interview. She said that they asked her six questions:

1. What is your GPA and can you handle this coursework?
2. What is your experience and can you perform in this environment?
3. Can you afford school and support yourself without working?
4. Can you afford school and support yourself without working?
5. Can you afford school and support yourself without working?
6. Can you afford school and support yourself without working?

The majority of nursing students take out Federal Student Loans (www.fafsa.ed.gov). It is likely that you are familiar with this option if you have been in nursing school for even a short time. These loans typically have low interest rates and are deferrable until you get out of school. Therefore, if you are already paying previously acquired loans, it may be possible to put those on hold until you finish your Master's Degree.

You can usually borrow an amount more than what your tuition is, to cover the cost of books and incidentals. The U.S. Department of Education's--Federal Student Aid website (www.studentaid.ed.gov) has a wealth of information available. You can find out information for financial aid availability, eligibility requirements, and repayment. Another valuable internet resource for student aid is Students.gov (www.students.gov). Here, you can find information on scholarships and grants, finding a loan, military funding, budgeting, and more.

There might be state aid offered that is worth looking in to. You can search for this at www.ed.gov; use the navigation linked to Graduate Study and Adult Learning. Of course, as websites are updated and changed, these links and options may change as well. All of the resources referenced to here are fairly easy to navigate, most having links directly to Graduate Degree seeking students. There are usually search functions within the site, where you can look for specific information related to nursing.

One of the best sites specific to nursing professionals needing financial aid is The U.S Department of Health and Human Services--Health Resources and Services Information (http://bhpr.hrsa.gov/dsa/index.htm). Here you can find out about loans and scholarships for disadvantaged students, nursing loans and scholarships, and many other resources for the health profession.

There are loan repayment programs available that repay student loans. Usually required for these is a commitment on your part to work for a certain amount of time in an area where there is a critical shortage of nurses. This also applies for some nursing scholarship programs. Information can usually be obtained from the financial aid department of the university, or directly through the nursing department at the institution that you are applying to. Graduate Assistantships may be available, but are usually not recommended or awarded because the time and energy needed for the anesthetist program would preclude the student from meeting the school's requirements for the assistantship contract.

One option for many going to CRNA school has been to have an Anesthesiology Group stipend their education throughout the program for a commitment of employment post-graduation. This opportunity may be easy to find, or it may be like finding a needle in a haystack; but it doesn't hurt to poke around, ask some questions, and put yourself in a position for finding that needle. A lot depends on where you are located, and, as said before, supply/demand of available CRNAs. If the group recognizes that they may have an upcoming shortage, they may be more inclined to go this route.

Another option may be your employer. Some hospital systems offer tuition payment programs. One difficulty here is that most expect you to work full time while they are reimbursing or paying for your schooling. Of course, this will not be an option in this program. On the other hand, there may be some programs set up for situations such as yours, so contact your human resources department and inquire.

As stated previously, you will have much expenditure. You will have to pay for liability insurance, books, uniforms, certifications (BLS/ACLS/PALS), and maintain your nursing license(s). You may have to buy specialty items, like a PDA, nerve stimulator, and ear molds. You will likely be required to maintain health insurance. You may have organization fees. Finally, there may be miscellaneous testing fees and the Board Exam after graduation.

Some suggestions for financial success might be to pay off your credit cards prior to starting the program. Do not close them though, for this will usually harm your FICO score, which is how many financial institutions determine credit worthiness. Maintain a good credit rating while you are preparing to enter this field, and if it is less than perfect, get a copy of your credit report and see if you can refute errors and make corrections. In an emergency, the available credit may come in handy. Also, if you need to take out a personal loan, or have an unavoidable expense arise, it will give you the best opportunity to find a lender that will offer you a good interest rate. Remember, you won't be working, so finding a creditor after quitting your job may be a challenge.

Some may have equity in their home or real estate, enabling the option of a home equity line of credit or a secondary mortgage. Just remember to budget yourself and make sure that you are not digging a hole that you can't climb out of. Most lenders will take into consideration your future earning potential. Do not rely on this though, since there is no guarantee that you are going to complete this goal. As far as they are concerned, a strong desire, unwavering persistence, and four dollars, will only get you a hamburger.

Try to get your monthly bills as low as you can. Pay your car off if possible. The sacrifice of driving an older model car and living in a cheaper apartment will be rewarded in the future with job security and the satisfaction of achieving an admirable goal. Oh, and you can probably get a nicer car later, too.

Chapter Eight

Acceptance

Chapter Eight

Acceptance

"Uh-Oh! What do I do now?" You will likely have a myriad of emotions; excitement, fear, and relief are all normal. What you won't have is doubt, because you will be prepared. You wouldn't have made it this far in the process if you weren't competent and capable of the task at hand. Stand tall and give yourself a pat on the back.

After calling all of your family, friends, and peers, allowing them to share in your success and be enviable of your future, it is time to come back down to earth and return to working toward your goals. There are some things that you should consider doing prior to starting the program.

Depending on the school, there is usually a sizable period of time from acceptance to the start of the program. This time may be as short as six months, or as long as two years. This in itself should be considered when looking into this career and all that it entails. Most people don't plan two months ahead, so the mere fact that you may have to wait for a year or longer to actually start a program shows a strong motivation.

To dissuade those that may be applying because they just want to see if they can get in, or are not certain if they truly want to go, upon notification of acceptance you may have to make a financial commitment, sending a check with your agreement of acceptance that will be applied to your fees at the start of the program. So be prepared financially, even before the program starts.

My suggestion to you now is this: Get Healthy!

Consider the following areas of your life, and determine ways to make healthy decisions in each of these:

- Physical
- Relational
- Emotional
- Social
- Spiritual
- Intellectual
- Financial

What are your goals? It may be a good idea to write them down. Have a six month, a two year, and a five year goal that are all well defined. As you need motivation throughout your day to make the best choices for your life, ask yourself (placing in each blank the seven above mentioned areas of health):

1. How is this action going to (or what did I do today to) increase my _____ Health?

2. What did I do today that was against my _____ Health?

3. What am I going to do tomorrow to get me closer to my goal of _____ Health?

I will give a few examples of what I mean. Let's start with Physical Health. How can you make healthier decisions in your life physically? I suggest exercising regularly if you don't already. I shouldn't have to mention the positive effects of being in good physical shape, such as increased endurance, self esteem, intellectual acuity, and decreased incidence of depression and stress. CRNA school is physically and emotionally demanding. You will be putting in long hours, getting less sleep than you are used to, and doing a job that is taxing on your body.

What I am going to say next is probably politically incorrect, but in many cases we ARE judged by our appearance. I am not saying that being overweight or out of shape will preclude you from getting in to or being successful in this career. But being in good physical shape doesn't usually happen without dedication and purpose. This positive attribute may be considered when evaluating you as a candidate.

Now is the time to correct errors, such as poor eating habits or cigarette smoking. If you smoke, and want to stop, do it now. Don't tell yourself that you are going to quit "as soon as you start school"; this will lead you to frustration and, very likely, a failed goal that will probably be exacerbated by the stress of the program.

If you wear glasses, or feel that you may have any issues with your vision, get checked. You will be doing a large amount of reading and computer work, which will put a strain on even a person with perfect vision. If you need glasses, get a pair, and wear them. If you already wear glasses, make sure that you are wearing the prescription that you need. Eyes change over time and those glasses you bought six years ago may not be the best ones for you now. It would be a shame if you made it all the way through school and became blind because of all the reading you have done. Of course I am exaggerating, but you get the idea.

What about your Relational Health? I have met a peer that went through a divorce during her first semester as an SRNA. She also has three children all under ten years of age, which she had primary custody of. She was able to finish without having to postpone completion. I do not suggest this for you though. If you have relationship difficulties, try, if you can, to amend them prior to the start of the program. The last thing you want is to be an emotional basket case before clinicals or class.

I remember hearing before getting in to nursing school that if you had relationship problems going in, you would more than likely be divorced before getting out. CRNA school is even more demanding on a relationship, so do what you can to put yourself in the least stressful of environments if possible. I know that this is difficult; building a solid relationship is one of the most challenging areas of life for most, but do the best that you can. Be smart. A friend of mine has a philosophy, "If you have a conflict or struggle between your head and your heart, follow your head".

What I have found is that this usually ends up happening whether you like it or not.

This same philosophy can be applied to your social relationships as well. Keep your close friends close, and be cautious with the external drama of those questionable relationships.

Intellectual Health should be ongoing. Continue reading and preparing yourself for the upcoming challenges. If you can take some of the class work while you are waiting, such as co-requisites, do so. Keep familiarizing yourself with general concepts and knowledge that you will soon be applying. If you work in CVICU, admit as many of the heart operations post-operatively as possible.

At this point, I think it is only fair to mention that it is my hope that I will be accepted to the CRNA program this year. Everything that I have written, the knowledge that I have acquired, has come from personal experience, research, and speaking with well-informed people already in this field or some way related to it. This information that I am sharing with you is from years of notes, asking questions, and paying attention to the right people at the right time. I remember how frustrating it was to me, finding out these bits of great advice, one or two ideas at a time. I am not sure why this book has not been written by someone else before me, but luckily for me, and hopefully luckily for you, I was given the opportunity. The response that I have received from those reading it prior to printing was typically, "Wow, I wish I would have had something like this when I was trying to get accepted!" Well, so do I. Now, you do.

One question that I am asked is this: If this book really is effectual, increasing the reader's likelihood of getting into a program, and if EVERYONE applying read this book, logically wouldn't that make this book ineffective in increasing the reader's chances? My answer is that if this occurred, it would likely do a few things: It may increase the overall ability of the applicant pool by influencing some strong intellectually and clinically superior nurses that may have been uncertain of this as a career, giving them the motivation to go ahead and give one-hundred percent. It may present more, better prepared applicants. Therefore, it might amplify the initial knowledge base of those applying to, or starting into a program.

Also, it may dissuade some of the weaker or less motivated applicants that were unsure of the challenges and what they were really getting themselves into. This may get them on a more appropriate path in their nursing career sooner, increasing their own value to the paradigm of nursing, whatever that may be.

So, my desire is that this book will ultimately raise the bar even higher for the profession of Certified Registered Nurse Anesthetists. The overall trend in America seems to be a lowering of the standards. Can we stand out even more impressively as a profession? I say yes! And more importantly, will we be able to offer to our clients in the future better outcomes than we do now? I sincerely hope that this is the case.

I also hope that on the next edition and printing of this book, I have the initials SRNA or CRNA behind my name. Wish me good luck and good skill.

Chapter Nine

Didactic

Chapter Nine
Didactic

The next two chapters discuss what it is like to be in both the classroom and clinical environments. Upon the completion of this program, you will be granted a Master's Degree in Science (MSN). Therefore, you will be expected to do graduate level work, including research, extensive reading, and professional development.

It is expected that the requirements for entrance to the program sufficiently ensure that the student has the necessary baseline knowledge to advance as a graduate student. Most undergraduate BSN programs require a solid foundation of core nursing knowledge, science, and math. Anatomy and physiology, microbiology, chemistry, statistics, and research are all going to be applied and built upon. Comprehension in pharmacologic principles will also be advanced.

One suggestion that I spoke of earlier is that you purchase some used books. Given the necessity of gaining nursing experience and the fact that a number of nurses get their BSN degrees in bridge programs from an Associate Degree, it is likely that many choosing to apply for CRNA school have been out of a majority of these classes for a while. If it has been years since you have taken A & P or chemistry, purchase a cheap book on these topics and refresh your memory.

Prior to the program starting, or shortly thereafter, you will be given a list of books to purchase. This will be a long list, an expensive list. You should anticipate it to be at or above two thousand dollars. You may not have to purchase all of these at one time, but more than likely you will. This is an accelerated program, considering all that you have to learn in two to three years.

If you have connections with students graduating, it may be possible to purchase some of the titles from them. Most practitioners will want to keep their library though, knowing that they will use it in the future. Make sure that you have the required book list by the institution before doing this, in case they make changes to titles or editions.

As new faculty come on, they may prefer different texts or authors, or they may even be authors of the texts. In that case they will surely be pushing for theirs to be used. The online methods discussed earlier may be effective for acquiring some of these. Some college bookstores may give you a moderate discount if you make the entire purchase from them, making it easier and saving you time, which may be more valuable then saving a few dollars.

What type of things will you be learning? Well, anesthesia stuff right? If it were only that simple!

Where do I start? Well, how about the beginning? You will learn about the history of anesthesia medicine, advancements in technology and pharmaceutical breakthroughs.

You will learn about the equipment used and the environment it is used in. You will be expected to know the physics and mechanics of the anesthesia machine(s). You will become familiar with the operating room, including hardware, placement of medical devices, airflow, infection control, and much more. The monitoring devices are learned. Also, it is important to understand the role and function of the entire intraoperative team, so that you can adequately assess the environment and potential complications.

The student is taught basic and advanced principles of anesthesia. This includes in-depth chemistry, physics, and biology. Of course, pharmacology is a large part of this field. The understanding of all of these topics is at the micro, or cellular level.

You will learn to more accurately recognize and manage electrolyte and acid-base imbalances. Fluid management will be addressed, correlated to specific disease processes. The treatment for some types of cases is the inverse for others. For example, with neurosurgical cases, it may be necessary to keep the patient mildly hypovolemic, even giving hypertonic solutions to decrease intracranial pressure. The opposite may be true in cardiac cases, when it is important the patient has adequate intravascular volume.

There will be class work on statistics and it's relation to biology, or Biostatistics. This will be used in conjunction with the review of current theoretical research, as well as possible research projects and theory development of your own. This may be required in the form of a Thesis or professional project to be completed prior to graduation. As with the undergraduate program, professional development is integrated into the curriculum. One of nursing's contributing factors to the public is its compassionate practice and active involvement in social issues. This is one reason that your community involvement prior to admission is so important. The role of the advanced practice nurse is not only to progress the practice of nursing; it is to improve the health and wellness of the society for which it performs such duties. The CRNA is included in this mission.

One way to do this is through understanding health policy and the economy of medicine. Keeping current with issues related to this field will be encouraged and expected. An active involvement in organizations locally and nationally should be considered. It may be required to become a member of the American Association of Nurse Anesthetists; even if it is not, you should become a member. The cost for graduate students is significantly discounted, making it easily affordable.

You will learn anesthesia principles and processes related to many areas, including: Obstetrical, pediatric, neurological, cardiovascular, and pulmonary. Anatomy, physiology, and pathophysiology will be covered, along with specific considerations from the anesthetist's perspective. Issues related to trauma, genitourinary, gastrointestinal, renal disease, endocrine disease, and orthopedic injury will be covered. In each disease process or surgical need, the necessity to customize the care plan to age specific requirements, especially pediatric and geriatric, will be discussed. This, of course, is not a comprehensive listing, but gives an idea of the coursework.

You will learn about regional anesthetic and analgesia techniques, including: Spinal, epidural, caudal blocks, and peripheral nerve blocks. Most of these procedures can be done without loss of independent respiratory functioning, making it safer for the patient. Also, pain management is becoming an ever increasing part of anesthesia medicine. This includes both acute and chronic pain issues. You may be required in your clinical experience to round with the pain management team, assessing needs of the patient.

A physical assessment and history review of the client will be very important tools utilized. This information will be used to guide you, alerting you to possible complications. Therefore, you will be expected to be proficient at doing an H & P (history and physical), taking into consideration anesthesia specific concerns, such as malignant hyperthermia in the familial history, or reactions to anesthesia such as nausea and vomiting post operatively. This way you can make accommodations to prophylactically treat for potential troubles.

You must be adept at CPR and ACLS protocols. As stated earlier, in cases where you are transferring patients from the OR to the ICU (or anywhere for that matter, including intraoperatively), a patient may cardiac arrest and you will need to lead the code. Remember, this action is also an act of patient advocacy. As the creed states, "First, do no harm." Being skillful in life saving situations such as these will give the patient what they need at the most vulnerable of times- an expert practitioner with his or her safety and best interest in the forefront of their mind. When you are in the clinical environment, the culmination of didactic knowledge comes together with the care of the patient.

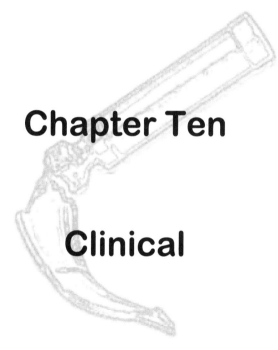

Chapter Ten

Clinical

Chapter Ten
Clinical

According to the American Association of Nurse Anesthetists' website, "The average student nurse anesthetist works at least 1,694 clinical hours and administers more than 790 anesthetics." Again, every program will be different and have unique expectations. Some will front load the didactics, with the majority of the clinicals done towards the end of the program. Some integrate the clinicals slowly, but early in the curriculum. There are pros and cons to each of these, but the end result is the same; a lot work will be done and the necessary experience will be gained.

You will likely be doing 8 to 12 hour days, 32 to 40 hours a week. Prior to entering the clinical environment, you will be introduced to anesthetic techniques and concepts. There may be labs, where you can hone your skills prior to implementation of new knowledge, such as in intubation and line placement. This is where the benefit of the human simulator will come in. Just like nursing school, initially, you will be given opportunity to attempt some of the common invasive skills prior to actually applying it to another human being. But, this program is very advanced and before you know it, you will be full speed ahead.

You will rotate in specialties areas, some of which are: Trauma, Pediatrics, Neruo, Obstetrics (Labor and Delivery), GI (Gastrointestinal), and CV (cardiovascular). The main objective is to give you experience with patients of all age groups, using the wide-ranging anesthetic techniques and technology available to today's practitioner.

The reading and work that you will be doing for clinicals will supersede the amount that you did for the class work. Take for instance if you are doing a CV rotation; you will likely have access to what you will be doing the next day in clinical. You may know who the anesthesiologist(s) or CRNA(s) are that you will be working with. You might have access to the surgical schedule, giving you a listing of the procedures that you will be performing anesthetic management for. In this case, you will be expected to be educated on the anatomy and pathophysiology for each of these procedures and diagnoses.

You will need to know commonly used anesthetic techniques, patient placement, possible complications, and other pertinent information for the procedure. An example of this is needing to know the difference in afterload/preload with a patient presenting with aortic stenosis versus one that has mitral regurgitation. The pharmacological interventions you use in one type of case may be contraindicated in another. If your preceptor is good, he or she will ask you questions, guiding you and educating you along the way. It is imperative that you not only know what to do, but that you know why you are doing what it is you are doing.

In addition to the requisite reading and research, you will have to do anesthesia care plans. I know what you are saying, "Oh no, not more care plans!" Sorry to be the bearer of bad news. Also, you will need to know the drugs that you will be using, especially if they are ones that are specific to the specialty area you are doing and are not very familiar. As stated previously in chapter four, you will need to know: classification, indications for use, mechanism of action, pharmacokinetics, contraindications, adverse reactions and side effects, interactions, route and dosage, and assessment/frequency of monitoring.

You will be doing clinical rotations at numerous hospitals as well. Some equipment will be different from site to site. You will need to familiarize yourself with the environment, where supplies are located, protocols, location of the pharmacy, facility specific documentation, and other important things.

At this point, if you haven't already, you will meet your patient. You will do a physical assessment on him/her, noting especially their physical frame (i.e. obese, short neck, landmarks), age, dentition, and possibility for airway complications. You will review their chart, noting their medical history, allergies, and complications to previous anesthesia by themselves or anyone in their family. You will evaluate pre-op lab values, x-rays, EKG, and other diagnostic information. Have they been NPO? What are their co-existing disease processes?

Consent for anesthesia must be signed if it already hasn't been. You will appropriately describe the anesthesia technique taking in to consideration the patient's learning needs and ability to communicate, as well as any cultural issues that may be pertinent. When possible, you want to reassure the patient (and family); placing them at ease by letting them know that they are in competent, capable, and compassionate hands.

Once the patient is in the operating room and placed on the table, the processes of induction of anesthesia, intubation and correct patient positioning will take place. You will assess IV access, ensuring patency for the initial sedating/paralyzing agent(s). Depending on the patient's risk for a complicated intubation, it may be necessary to keep the patient awake during this procedure. The appropriate laryngoscope blade will be chosen, as well as endotracheal tube size and length (ensuring that the inflatable cuff is functioning properly). After hyper-oxygenating the patient and visualizing the vocal cords, the ETT is placed and checked for placement. This is done by auscultation of lung fields, visualization of the chest wall, and pulse oximetry/CO_2 monitoring. If the intubation was difficult and required a laryngoscopy, visualization of the tracheal cartilage and carina (where the bronchus bifurcate) will be possible. Anesthesia of the patient is maintained.

Monitoring the patient with indicators such as ECG, pulse oximetry, CO_2, temperature, renal functioning (catheter), and an automated blood pressure cuff will be ongoing. It may be necessary, depending on the procedure, to have invasive monitoring, such as continuous arterial blood pressure monitoring, central venous pressure, and pulmonary artery pressure. If this is the case, it may be necessary to place an arterial line and/or central line. In some very difficult cases, such as craniotomies, it may be necessary to have continuous doppler monitoring of the heart to listen for venous air embolism, which can cause severe acute injury to the patient if an air aspiration catheter is not used. I can say that in all of my years in nursing, I have never seen someone work so hard as the CRNA I once witnessed doing a craniotomy case.

Proper patient placement is imperative. Improper placement, even minutely, can cause permanent injury to the patient. It is the responsibility of the entire surgical team to be cognizant of an improperly placed patient, but it is the anesthetist's job. Each surgical intervention may require different positioning requirements. The patient may need to be placed supine, or laterally. It is important to recognize the potential for peripheral nerve injury, or tissue ischemia due to pressure or improper placement. One CRNA offered this advice when it comes to patient placement, "Get paranoid early in your career, and stay that way for a long time". I think what he meant was to be vigilant, but the point stuck. Remember, you must be the patient advocate when they are at their most vulnerable.

As all of this is going on, you are monitoring the patient's pulmonary and cardiovascular status. It may help if you have eyes on the back of your head, so that you can do two things at once. But until have this gift, you'll have to make do with attentive observation and intuition. This job is not impossible though; there are tens of thousands of anesthetists that do this on a daily basis. You can, too.

After the surgical procedure is completed, the process of weaning off of the anesthesia and ventilator (depending on the type of case) is accomplished. This, if appropriate, leads to extubation of the patient, and eventual transfer to the post-anesthesia care unit, or PACU. In some cases, open heart surgery for instance, the patient will remain intubated and be transferred to the intensive care unit where they will be placed on the ventilator and monitored even more closely. It is the job of the anesthetist to accompany and manage the patient in transport to the ICU, ensuring that adequate ventilation and hemodynamic stability are maintained. Report will be given to the nurse(s) assuming care of the patient, including: drugs given, procedure done, potential needs and complications, and other pertinent information that may make the transition safe for the patient.

Finally, after all of this is done and your charting is completed, it's time to go to the pharmacy to pick up meds for your next surgery. If you are lucky, you may have time to eat some peanut butter and have a cup of water before you have to set up for your next case. Don't drink too much water though! You don't want to have an intraoperative anesthetist 'bladder emergency'.

As with any job in nursing, or any occupation for that matter, you will have good days and bad days. You will have easy days that you thought were going to be difficult, and difficult days that you thought were going to be easy. That is all a part of nursing, and should not dissuade you. There are enough options as a CRNA, that if you are not happy doing what you are doing, you can move around until you find something that fits you personally. It may be with a team of other CRNA's. It may be working in an outpatient facility. It may be traveling around the country doing independent contracting work. Or maybe you may be interested in going abroad, working outside of the United States. Maybe you have considered teaching. The point is, this degree, this certification making you a professional Certified Registered Nurse Anesthetist, will bring value to your career and autonomy and power to your individual future career path.

The decision is yours. Hopefully the information in this book has created a more informed applicant, setting the stage for you to transform your dreams into reality, making the world a safer place to go to 'SLEEP'.

Chapter Eleven

Resources

Chapter Eleven
Resources

World Wide Web

The following is a short listing of web resources previously cited throughout this book. Another suggestion not mentioned earlier is the use of online Blogging. For those that are not familiar, a blog is similar to a journal or diary entry. There are many CRNAs and SRNAs that keep blogs of their experiences. If you do a web search with combinations of the key words {crna, blog, srna, nurse, anesthetist}, you will very likely come across blogs with wonderful information and experiences.

Also, at Myspace.com, there are nurse anesthetist groups that you can join. Many of the group members at Myspace are nursing students with aspirations of becoming CRNAs. This, in my opinion, is a great way to network with professionals and like minded students. Happy hunting!

Another great resource is Allnurses.com. This site has an online forum that is categorized by specialty. You can search through topics specific to SRNAs and CRNAs, allowing you access to current trends and issues concerning this field.

At the time of this writing, the links listed below are all active. But the internet changes at a very fast pace and these links may no longer be accurate by the time of printing. Therefore, it is suggested you do a web search if you find any links no longer working. Or, at **www.sleepwiththisbook.com**, there is a listing of these and other links, making it easy to navigate from site to site, as well as an online blog where you can post questions and read what others have written.

Allnurses.com
http://www.aacn.org

American Association of Colleges of Nursing (AACN)
http://www.aacn.nche.edu

American Association of Critical-care Nurses
http://www.aacn.org

American Association of Nurse Anesthetists
http://www.aana.com

American Heart Association
http://www.americanheart.org/

Anesthesiologist Assistant
http://www.anesthesiaassistant.com

Big Brother/Big Sisters
http://www.bbbsa.org

ECG information
http://www.ecglibrary.com

Education Testing Service
http://www.ets.org/gre

Free Application for Federal Student Aid
http://www.fafsa.ed.gov

Goodwill Industries International, Inc.
http://www.goodwill.org

Habitat for Humanity
http://www.habitat.org

Human Patient Simulator
http://www.meti.com

Millers Analogies Test
http://www.milleranalogies.com

Myspace.com
http://www.myspace.com/~~gonegray~~

Nurse Anesthetist (Blog, documents, library)
http://www.nurseanesthetist.org

Red Cross
http://www.redcross.org

Salvation Army
http://www.salvationarmyusa.org

Sleep with this Book
http://www.sleepwiththisbook.com

Student Gateway to the U.S. Government
http://www.students.gov

The International Federation of Nurse Anesthetists
http://www.ifna-int.org

The National Committee for Certifying Agencies (NCCA)
http://www.noca.org/ncca/accredorg.htm

The National League for Nursing Accrediting Commission
http://www.nlnac.org

The U.S. Department of Education's Council of Post Secondary Education (COPA).
http://www.ope.ed.gov/accreditation

U.S. Department of Education's--Federal Student Aid
http://www.studentaid.ed.gov

U.S. Department of Health and Human Services-- Health Resources and Services Information
http://bhpr.hrsa.gov/dsa/index.htm

United Way
http://www.unitedway.org

Volunteer Match
http://www.volunteermatch.org

World Federation of Societies of Anaesthesiologists
http://www.world-anaesthesia.org

<u>Book Purchase Suggestions</u>

The following is a short list of books that I found on Amazon.com and Half.com. Remember to look for past editions of these titles if you are simply using them for resources. This will save you a lot of money, offering almost the same information.

I am not suggesting that you get all of the following books. What I am suggesting it that you purchase a book or two just to familiarize yourself with the type of information that you will be expected to know, hopefully making you more aware pre-acceptance to pertinent information and experiences.

Basics of Anesthesia
By Robert R. Stoelting and Ronald D. Miller
-If you only purchase one book, get this one.

Introduction to General, Organic & Biochemistry
By Bettelheim, Brown, & March
-Or similar chemistry refresher text

Clinical Anesthesiology
By G. Edward Morgan & Maged S. Mikhail

Handbook of Clinical Anesthesia
By Barash, Cullen, & Stoelting

Handbook of Nurse Anesthesia
By Nagelhout, Zaglaniczny, & Haglund, Jr.

Clinical Anesthesia Procedures of the Massachusetts General Hospital
By Davidson, Eckhardt III, & Perese
-This book is required by most programs

Renal Physiology
By Arthur J. Vander

Pulmonary Physiology
By Michael G. Levitzky

Cardiovascular Physiology
By David Mohrman and Lois Jane Heller

Certification Review in Nurse Anesthesia
By Wynne Waugaman & Scot Foster
(In a certification review book, you will see examples of what the expectations at the completion of the program will be)

Springhouse Review for Critical Care Nursing Certification: An indispensable study guide for the C.C.R.N. exam

Michael Gray, RN, BSN

Author:

Michael Gray, RN, BSN

Contact at:

Michael@gonegray.com